Forgiveness

A COLORING JOURNAL SUPPORTING YOUR JOURNEY TO FREEDOM

COURTNEY B. DUNLAP, M.S.

Cover photo by Jeremy Bishop from Pexels.
Front and back cover designs by Courtney B. Dunlap.
Written and designed by Courtney B. Dunlap.
Editing services provided by Casey Potter.
Consultations provided by Kim C. Lee and Renée Barry.
Author headshots by Pascale Mobley.

Stories for Us LLC
Sicklerville, NJ

For ordering information:
www.courtneybdunlap.com

First Edition

Dedication:

I dedicate this book to you!

I know I'm not alone on my own forgiveness journey.

The countless conversations through mentorship,
coaching, couples' counseling, and other church
ministry I've done for over a decade, has shown me this.
Many of the people I've supported were simply trying
to muster up the courage to embrace forgiveness once more.

Because of this, I know the fight for forgiveness
is not one that should be fought alone!

I stand with you.

But, I'll do you one better...

God fights **for** you!

Be encouraged!

Congratulations are in order!

You may find it odd to be congratulated in a coloring journal focused on forgiveness.

Congratulations are in order because you are about to embark upon a journey that many people run from their entire lives!
If I can be honest, there were times when I also ran from the hard soul work of forgiveness.

You see, forgiveness is a journey.

Over the course of one's life, forgiveness can have many faces.
There is simply no one way to forgive.

Forgiveness is also not easy.
In fact, forgiveness can be messy, confusing, and quite complicated.

In all this, the single hope I hold on to is that though forgiveness is not easy, forgiveness IS possible!

Hence, the reason for this book.

My prayer is that you will know this to be true down to your very core!
This book is just one more step in support of your life's journey of forgiveness.
I truly believe forgiveness leads to freedom for all who seek it!

There is hope, joy, and peace ahead if you choose to put one foot in front of the other.
This coloring journal is meant to be therapeutic, reflective, and enjoyable.
It is also meant to be intentional.

You will find coloring pages and guided journal prompts inviting you to stop, think, and reflect.
I hope you will have honest realizations about what forgiveness can look like for you.
I pray you to find hope in Christ and peace with God along the way!

Many blessings to you, and I look forward to seeing you on the other side!

With hope,

Courtney

LAM·EN·TA·TION

noun:
the passionate
expression of grief or
sorrow; weeping

Forgiveness cannot happen until we face our hurt.
Use this space to journal about who or what hurt you.

I'm hurt because...

_____

_____

_____

_____

_____

_____

_____

_____

_____

_____

_____

_____

_____

_____

_____

_____

_____

_____

_____

_____

_____

DON'T *turn away* from me in my time of *distress.* bend down to listen.

Psalm 102:2

Many times, anger is a natural emotion when we feel hurt.
Use the section below to journal about your anger.

I'm angry because...

_____

_____

_____

_____

_____

_____

_____

_____

_____

_____

_____

_____

_____

_____

_____

_____

_____

_____

_____

I'm disappointed because...

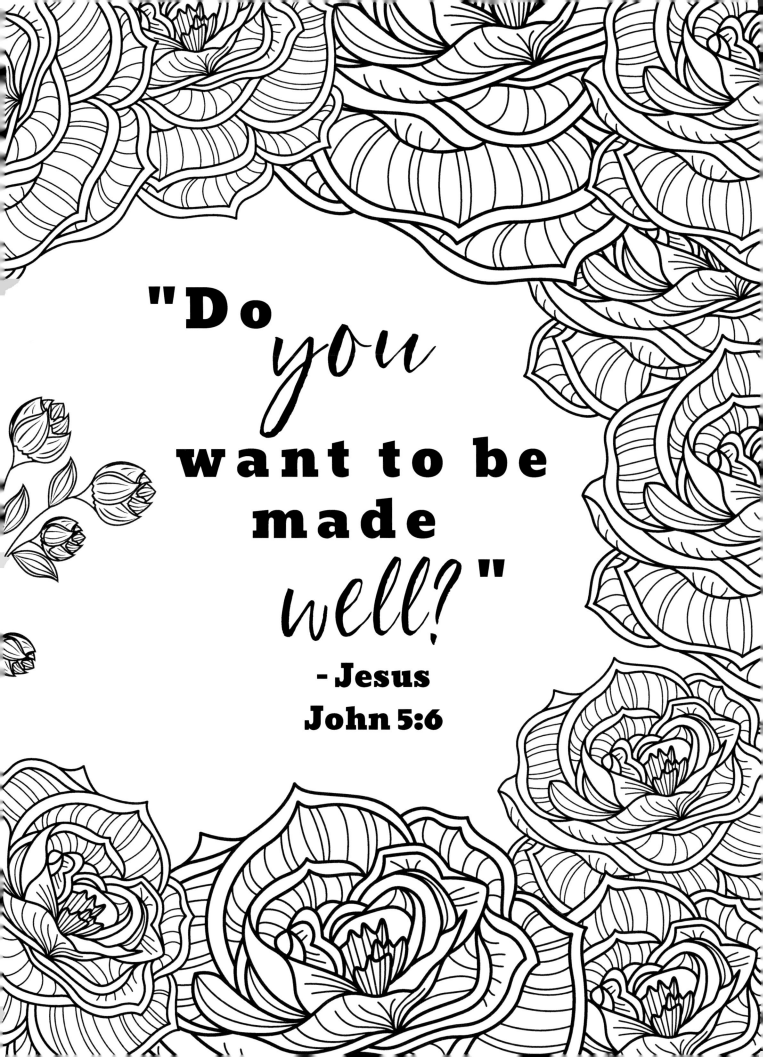

"Do you want to be made well?"

- Jesus
John 5:6

Sometimes our hurt, anger, and disappointment distract us from what can make us well.
Reflect and write about what you must do to be well.

_____

_____

_____

_____

_____

_____

_____

_____

_____

_____

_____

_____

_____

_____

_____

_____

_____

_____

_____

_____

_____

_____

CON·FES·SION

noun:

a formal admission of one's sins with repentance and desire of absolution

The sad news is that sin has invaded our world.
Sin is the breaking of God's perfect law.
God is perfect and cannot be around sin.
All people have sinned.
Sinners hurt other sinners.
Sin must be punished.
The punishment for sin is separation from God.

The good news is Jesus died to take our punishment for sin.
When people believe Jesus died in their place,
they can escape punishment for their sins.
They can experience freedom from sin.
This is the gospel.

"BUT if we CONFESS OUR sins to GOD, He can ALWAYS be TRUSTED to forgive US."

1 JOHN 1:9

24

Sometimes, our hurt makes it challenging to see and confess any of our own sin.
Reflect on your hurt heart. If any sin is present, use this space to confess it.

I confess...

_____

_____

_____

_____

_____

_____

_____

_____

_____

_____

_____

_____

_____

_____

_____

_____

_____

_____

_____

_____

_____

Jesus

DIED SO I CAN

live!

FOR·GIVE·NESS

noun:

the action or process of forgiving

Forgiveness was never meant to be an isolated occurrence.
Write about the last time you chose to forgive someone.

_____

_____

_____

_____

_____

_____

_____

_____

_____

_____

_____

_____

_____

_____

_____

_____

_____

_____

_____

_____

_____

"**FORGIVE** *as the Lord* **forgave** *you.*"

Colossians 3:13

"For if
YOU
forgive other people when
they sin against you,
YOUR HEAVENLY FATHER
will also forgive you."
MATTHEW 6:15

I

CAN

CHOOSE!

Freedom

noun:

the power or right to act, speak, or think as one wants without hindrance or restraint

"IT IS FOR *freedom* THAT CHRIST *has set us free.*"

GALATIONS 5:1

The journey of forgiveness brings freedom.
We are hurt, but we can forgive. We hurt others, yet they forgive us.
Reflect on what you have been freed from here.

I am free from...

_____

_____

_____

_____

_____

_____

_____

_____

_____

_____

_____

_____

_____

_____

_____

_____

_____

_____

_____

"You have been set free from sin."

Romans 6:22

PRAISE
noun:

the offering of grateful homage in words or song, as an act of worship

The burdens we carry are lifted when we forgive and are forgiven.
We can praise and thank God for this. What can you thank and praise God for right now?

I praise God...

"Oh lord, I will honor and praise YouR name."

Isaiah 25:1

HOPE

noun:

a feeling of expectation for a certain thing to happen

"AS FOR *me*
I WILL
always HAVE
hope!"

PSALM 71:14

53

The journey of forgiveness may not yet be complete in your life.
If so, that's okay!
Even still, what are you hopeful for right now?

I hope...

where flowers grow ...

So does hope!

Acknowledgments:

Thank you to my pain.
This journey of forgiveness is owed to you. I am better for it. I am still
learning the hard truth that forgiveness is not easy,
but it is possible!

Thank you, Curtis, for patiently walking with me as I learn to forgive and
release those who have deeply wounded me. Thank you for never hurrying
me along. Your kindness and gentle care for my soul during some of my
lowest points has been a healing balm. I would have never known it had God
not given me you.
So, I thank you!

To our babies, mommy loves you! I pray that you will learn more about our
Heavenly Father's deep love and forgiveness towards us as you watch me
travel along my own forgiveness journey.

To my circle, my trusted few...you know who you are. You have been loving
and wise travel companions along this road.
Thank you!

Jesus, thank You for loving me in spite of me! Thank You for dying to
forgive me for my own blind spots and transgressions against others and
You! Your unending love is one I will never fully grasp!

Yet, all I can say is, "Thank You!"

About the Author

Courtney B. Dunlap is the author of *The Rumble Hunters* and its companion coloring activity book!

Courtney shares stories for the dignity of all people from the truth of God's word through her independent publishing imprint, Stories for Us LLC.

Courtney writes and edits content for LifeWay Christian Resources. Courtney homeschools her children and is passionate about empowering other homeschooling families. She does this through a blog called Able to Teach Homeschool Collective. Courtney is married to Curtis, and they share four beautiful children.

Courtney has a B.S. in Psychology from Rutgers University and an M.S. in Christian Counseling from Cairn University. Her training in these areas and her own journey of forgiveness helped shape this book.

Courtney speaks nationally and internationally to
celebrate the dignity God has given all people.
She inspires Black and Brown people to know that
their stories are worthy of being told!

For speaker inquires, email: hello@courtneybdunlap.com

This coloring journal offers joy and rest in God.
God judges justly despite this broken world. Jesus Christ came to live and die
for sinners, and Jesus offers forgiveness as the only way back to God.
Trusting in Jesus' perfect life, death, and resurrection will secure our only
hope for true freedom.

Won't you trust Jesus today?

Courtney's books are available everywhere books are sold.

They can also be purchased from her website, www.courtneybdunlap.com.

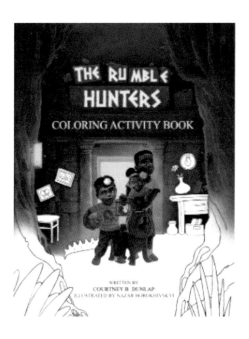